JEWELS OF WISDOM

A One-Year Weekly Journal

Julie
May these
jewels of wisdom
be a blessing to your
soul ~Carla 2022

Carla J. Olds

Jewels of Wisdom: A One-Year Weekly Journal

Cover Design by Coffee Cup Creatives.

Book Design by Coffee Cup Creatives.

Printed in the United States of America.

First Printing, 2020

Unless otherwise indicated, Scripture quotations are from the following versions of the The Holy Bible: New King James Version, King James Version, and New Living Translation.

For permission requests to use the materials in this book, write to the publisher, at the address below.

DW Creative Publishers

4261 E. University Dr. #30-355

Prosper, TX 75078

www.DWCreativePublishers.com

connect@dwcreativepublishers.com

Dedication

Many years ago, God inspired me to write a journal that would be utilized not just as a calendar but also as a devotional and prayer journal. This is such a beautiful way to begin a new plan with a new perspective. It is my hope that you use this as an intricate and intimate place to read scriptures, list prayer requests, and set goals.

I dedicate this book to God, and I am eternally grateful for the ways God continues to use me.

I dedicate this book to my parents, the late Deacon Malcolm & Phyllis Johnson, who taught me to plan and to always BE ON TIME!

I dedicate this book to my wonderful husband, and I am thankful for the man he is in my life.

I dedicate this book to my children. May God continue to supply all your needs according to God's riches in glory.

This Journal Belongs to:

_____

Week 1

Genesis 1:1 (NKJV): "In the beginning God created the heavens and the earth."

Weekly Devotional

God created. The word "created" is a verb which means to bring something new into existence. As you begin this year, let this year be one of creation for you. Business creation. Relationship creation.

Journal Your Thoughts

Week 2

John 1:1 (NKJV): "In the beginning was the Word, and the Word was with God, and the Word was God."

Weekly Devotional

It is comforting to know that whatever situation we find ourselves in, God is there with us. God's Word is always here to guide us. Whatever you need can be found in God's Word from finding a spouse and dealing with natural and bonus relatives to dealing with complications, consequences, and principalities. God is everywhere at the same time and God's Word is timeless.

Journal Your Thoughts

Week 3

Zechariah 4:10 (NLT "Do not despise these small beginnings, for the Lord rejoices to see the work begin..."

Weekly Devotional

In this scripture, the temple is being rebuilt. Before the temple was complete, the people began to complain because the temple wasn't as elaborate as Solomon's Temple. Don't despise what you currently see as small in the beginning. Once you give your plans to God, they will work out to be even more magnificent than you could have ever imagined.

Journal Your Thoughts

Week 4

Proverbs 3:9 (KJV): "Honour the Lord with thy substance, and with the firstfruits of all thine increase:"

Weekly Devotional

Always give God what He is due first! Time, energy, and resources are included in first fruits. Everything you need will flow out of the abundance that you'll receive after you've given God His portion. You will continue to always operate in the overflow. This week, intentionally make a shift and give God the first fruits of your time, energy and resources.

Journal Your Thoughts

Week 5

Job 8:7 (CSB): "Then, even if your beginnings were modest, your final days will be full of prosperity."

Weekly Devotional

After Job was stricken with sickness and multiple losses God replenished what he had even more abundantly. When we encounter life events, we can be reminded by those who went before us in the faith who also experienced similar challenges that God is fully capable of replenishing what we think we've lost. This week, seek areas in your life where there appears to be lack and allow God to replenish those areas in your life.

Journal Your Thoughts

Week 6

John 15:12 (NKJV): "This is My commandment, that you love one another as I have loved you."

Weekly Devotional

The Bible is a beautiful love story written to us by God. As God commands, we should earnestly love one another. There are times when it seems hard to love others, and it is at these times, when we must push ourselves to love more.

Journal Your Thoughts

John 15:13 (KJV): "Greater love hath no man than this, that a man lay down his life for his friends."

Weekly Devotional

As Christians, Jesus paid the ultimate sacrifice for us. He laid down His life so we could have new and abundant life. Sacrifice can seem like such a big word. When opportunities arise for us to sacrifice, it's best for us to sacrifice for others. Pray and seek wisdom when opportunities to make an ultimate sacrifice or long-term choice need to be made.

Journal Your Thoughts

Week 8

1 Corinthians 13:4 (NIV): "Love is patient, love is kind. It does not envy, it does not boast, it is not proud."

Weekly Devotional

When true love exists, we must adhere to some rules. Those rules include patience and kindness. It's interesting that this verse explicitly mentions what love is and what love is not. As we take a look at our relationships (business partners, friendships, and coworkers included) we should continually check and recheck our motives. Are we operating out of true love or are we becoming envious, boastful, and proud?

Journal Your Thoughts

Ephesians 4:2 (NIV): "Be completely humble and gentle; be patient, bearing with one another in love."

Weekly Devotional

There are changes in our lives that take place when true love is exhibited. True love seeks to offer assistance and is not negligent in the care of others. The characteristics of humility, gentleness and patience will be on display. As those characteristics are developed, it will become easier to support and love one another throughout our day-to-day activities.

Journal Your Thoughts

Week 10

Proverbs 3:5-6 (KJV): "Trust in the Lord with all thine heart; and lean not unto thine own understanding. In all thy ways acknowledge him, and he shall direct thy paths."

Weekly Devotional

Trust is one of those words that invoke calm in some people and calamity in others. During our lifetime, there will be certain people who we will trust and some who we won't. It's up to us to pray and ask God for wisdom and discernment when trusting others. Give your entire trust to the Lord. The Lord is the One who knows exactly what you are going through and how to appropriately handle your situation. Trust in the Lord and don't doubt as we lean not on our own understanding.

Journal Your Thoughts

Week 11

Psalm 56:3 (NIV): "When I am afraid, I put my trust in you."

Weekly Devotional

There are various times in our lives in which we will experience being afraid. It is during these times when our faith must remain greater than our fears. Know that God honors your faith and whatever is given to God is honored. If you trust in Him, God will take care of all your worries.

Journal Your Thoughts

Week 12

Jeremiah 29:11 (NIV): "For I know the plans I have for you," declares the Lord, "plans to prosper you and not to harm you, plans to give you hope and a future."

Weekly Devotional

You have likely heard the saying, "When you want to make God laugh, tell Him your plans." Along with the trust we place in the Lord, our faith should also inform the fact that the Lord knows the best plans for us. Those plans include our peace and wellbeing when we trust Him fully.

Journal Your Thoughts

1 Peter 5:7 (NIV): "Cast all your anxiety on him because he cares for you."

Weekly Devotional

When life sends trouble and worry your way, the best thing you can do is cast your cares on Jesus. As a fisherman casts his fishing rod in the water so should we also cast our cares and concerns on the One who cares for us. It's so comforting to know that God cares for you and all we need to do is give our worries over to Him.

Journal Your Thoughts

Week 14

Philippians 1:6 (KJV): "Being confident of this very thing, that he which hath begun a good work in you will perform it until the day of Jesus Christ:"

Weekly Devotional

Sometimes, life presents a challenge knowing God created you for a specific purpose. Due to life's unpredictability, we are unable to internalize and visualize what we know God has purposed in our hearts. God allows us to go through these trials and tribulations to resolve the necessary character flaws and heart issues that need to be perfected within us.

Journal Your Thoughts

Week 15

Isaiah 43:19 (NIV): "See, I am doing a new thing! Now it springs up; do you not perceive it? I am making a way in the wilderness and streams in the wasteland."

Weekly Devotional

Search inside your heart for the new things that God is creating within you and around you. When the Israelites were traveling from Egypt to Canaan a way was made for them as they moved through the desert. As God provided for them in the desert, God will also provide for us as well. The provision that God has typically provided for us will begin to look differently. Look for the new and different ways that God has provided for you. As your seasons and situations change so will the ways in which God provides.

Journal Your Thoughts

Week 16

2 Peter 3:13 (KJV): "Nevertheless we, according to his promise, look for new heavens and a new earth, wherein dwelleth righteousness."

Weekly Devotional

The Lord is surely coming! In the anticipation of the Lord's arrival, we are reminded of the promise that righteousness will dwell within this newness. Holy Week is the week of Jesus' triumphal entry. At the end of the week, Jesus was crucified, nailed to a cross and buried. As Christians, this is our week! This is the week of resurrection! Rejoice knowing that Jesus died for our sins and rose again! Praise God for anticipation – anticipation of the Second Coming. The Lord is surely coming again!

Journal Your Thoughts

Isaiah 65:17 (NIV): "See, I will create new heavens and a new earth. The former things will not be remembered, nor will they come to mind."

Weekly Devotional

The blessing in this scripture is that God reiterates that there will be a brand new heaven and a brand new earth. It's exciting to know that as God creates a brand new heaven and earth, God can create those same visions in our minds. As we endure obstacles in life, it's such a blessing to know that we can encounter the most horrific situations and God will still create newness. We are able to forget the former things and the things of old and they won't even come to mind or be remembered.

Journal Your Thoughts

Week 18

Romans 12:2 (KJV): "And be not conformed to this world: but be ye transformed by the renewing of your mind, that ye may prove what *is* that good, and acceptable, and perfect, will of God."

Weekly Devotional

It is hard to disconnect from social media. The people in our circles and the world is communicating on a daily basis. It becomes imperative that as Christians, we focus on biblical principles and values. Our lives will become a never-ending cesspool of nothingness if we continue to indulge fleshly pleasures as the world instructs us to do. Once our minds are changed and focused on what God has for us, we can begin the process of renewing our minds and transforming our lives. Once our minds are transformed, our lifestyle will follow.

Journal Your Thoughts

Week 19

Ephesians 4:24 (NIV): "And to put on the new self, created to be like God in true righteousness and holiness."

Weekly Devotional

Putting on the new self is a process that as Christians we should constantly be trying to achieve. It may seem impossible at times. The God we serve knows where we are in our relationship with Him. As we are "putting on" our new self, we are constantly becoming like Christ is in true righteousness and holiness.

Journal Your Thoughts

Week 20

Proverbs 31:30 (NIV): "Charm is deceptive, and beauty is fleeting; but a woman who fears the LORD is to be praised."

Weekly Devotional

We all possess beautiful physical characteristics. After all, we are made by God. When you have an intimate relationship with the Lord people around you will know it. Literally, God's anointing will begin to seep out of you and the physical characteristics you possess won't even matter. It is our anointing and God's power that makes the difference in our lives.

Journal Your Thoughts

Psalm 139:14 (NIV): "I praise you because I am fearfully and wonderfully made; your works are 0wonderful; I know that full well."

Weekly Devotional

As a child, I used to take this verse for granted. When I was bullied in middle school, my parents always repeated this verse to me. While traveling through this journey called life, we will often feel like we are less than. The wonderful thing about God's Word is that there is encouragement for every situation we encounter. When we rise in the morning, we should praise the Lord just because we are "fearfully and wonderfully made."

Journal Your Thoughts

Week 22

Ephesians 2:10 (NIV): "For we are God's handiwork, created in Christ Jesus to do good works, which God prepared in advance for us to do."

Weekly Devotional

Handiwork is something that is made or created for a specific purpose and is usually designed with intricate details. When someone crochets a blanket or some baby booties, the word "handiwork" comes to mind. As the person who is crocheting or cross-stitching takes their time in ensuring the intricate details are well done, we can be reminded that God does the same with us. God has taken the time to literally knit us together and knows each and every detail perfectly.

Journal Your Thoughts

Ecclesiastes 3:11 (NIV): "He has made everything beautiful in its time. He has also set eternity in the human heart; yet no one can fathom what God has done from beginning to end."

Weekly Devotional

There are two sets of time: God's timing and man's timing. This is referred to as *Kairos* and *Chronos* respectively in Greek. *Kairos* refers to the right moment or the most opportune time. *Chronos* refers to the chronological timing while *Kairos* is the indeterminate time in which everything happens. We often expect God to accomplish our "checklist" in a certain amount of time. When our trust is placed completely in God, we can rest assured that our *Chronos* and *Kairos* times will simultaneously align, and we will be offered the opportunity of a lifetime.

Journal Your Thoughts

Week 24

Proverbs 10:14 (NIV): "The wise store up knowledge, but the mouth of a fool invites ruin."

Weekly Devotional

The book of Proverbs is a wonderful place to start if you are in doubt about what to read in the Bible. Proverbs is often called "the book of wisdom." Wisdom is the ability to know what to say, how to say it, and when to say it. The wise person in this scripture has an intimate relationship with God and the fool is the one who is constantly "firing off" at the mouth. When you think before you speak, you attain positive results.

Journal Your Thoughts

Proverbs 3:7 (NKJV): "Do not be wise in your own eyes; Fear the Lord and depart from evil."

Weekly Devotional

Being wise in your own eyes is the inability to see someone else's perspective. The ultimate perspective we seek is that of the Lord's. As we look to God for answers in our continually changing culture and society, it is important that we first consult God in **_all_** we do. Big and small decisions are imperative and important to you and to God. Actively consult God on each decision you make.

Journal Your Thoughts

Week 26

Proverbs 24:3-4 (NIV): By wisdom a house is built, and through understanding it is established; through knowledge its rooms are filled with rare and beautiful treasures.

Weekly Devotional

Wisdom is a lifestyle. We must constantly use wisdom in our day-to-day activities. Balancing spirituality and common sense and knowing when and how to use both is called wisdom. Learning how to operate completely in God's wisdom is a process. It can be learned over time. This week, spend some time with the Lord and just ask God, "Show me how I can fully operate in Your wisdom."

Journal Your Thoughts

3 John 2 (KJV): "Beloved, I wish above all things that thou mayest prosper and be in health, even as thy soul prospereth."

Weekly Devotional

As children of God, it is refreshing to know that God has our best interests at heart. The definition of "prosper" is to flourish. With that definition, God wants us to flourish in all aspects of our lives. As our soul flourishes, God wants our minds and bodies to flourish as well. Studying the Word is not an option. Lack of obedience is not an option. We're halfway through the year, let's FLOURISH!

Journal Your Thoughts

Week 28

John 8:32 (NKJV): "And you shall know the truth, and the truth shall make you free."

Weekly Devotional

Truth and freedom go hand in hand. When you are capable of walking in the truth, not your own truth, but in God's truth, then you are also walking in true freedom. After we have released the secrets we have on our hearts to the Lord, then we can walk in ultimate freedom. Sure, there are aspects of our lives that we don't tend to readily share with others, but when you release your concerns to the Lord, you can walk in true freedom.

Journal Your Thoughts

John 8:36 (KJV): "If the Son therefore shall make you free, ye shall be free indeed."

Weekly Devotional

When we are walking in a consistent intimate relationship with Jesus, there is a sense of freedom that can't be explained. Our sense of how we operate in freedom is congruent to how Jesus wants us to feel as we experience this type of freedom. Freedom offers us options and walking with God definitely offers options. This week ask God to help you to walk with Him and experience a true freedom that offers lots of options and opportunities.

Journal Your Thoughts

Week 30

Romans 8:2 (NKJV): "For the law of the Spirit of life in Christ Jesus has made me free from the law of sin and death."

Weekly Devotional

Acknowledging that you are a sinner saved by God's grace is an amazing feat for some. There is comfort in knowing that God can receive me in all my mess and shortcomings. With all that, walking in God's Spirit has allowed me to operate in complete freedom. There is no sin too big or too small that the Lord won't forgive. This week hold your head high and walk in the freedom of that forgiveness.

Journal Your Thoughts

Week 31

Galatians 5:1 (NIV): "It is for freedom that Christ has set us free. Stand firm, then, and do not let yourselves be burdened again by a yoke of slavery."

Weekly Devotional

The definition of slavery is working without pay. As a Christian, we are fortunate that we receive our "pay" on a daily basis. Waking up every morning and having faith that God will take care of our daily needs is part of our freedom. This week remember that you are one of God's children and allow God to release you from your self-inflicted yoke that has prevented you from progressing in Christ.

Journal Your Thoughts

Habakkuk 2:3 (KJV): "For the vision is yet for an appointed time, but at the end it shall speak, and not lie: though it tarry, wait for it; because it will surely come, it will not tarry."

Weekly Devotional

God will give you visions and dreams. Ensuring that these visions and dreams come to fruition includes remembering that the vision is for an appointed time. Don't become discouraged and unfocused when it appears that you are not seeing the visions and dreams that God has placed in your heart come to pass. The vision will come at God's appointed time. God is intricately orchestrating the pieces that need to be placed together for a successful vision and dream to come to pass.

Journal Your Thoughts

Ecclesiastes 9:10 (NIV): "Whatever your hand finds to do, do it with all your might, for in the realm of the dead, where you are going, there is neither working nor planning nor knowledge nor wisdom."

Weekly Devotional

Whatever God has placed in your heart to do, do it will all your might. Focus on what God has for you to do. It is hard sometimes and distractions will come. Children, spouses, careers – all these areas of your life call for your undivided attention and it may seem like you are going to lose your mind. It's okay! Just realign yourself with what God has placed on your heart. Take some time this week to acknowledge before God what needs to be done so you may refocus and reclaim the energy needed to pursue the future God has planned for you.

Journal Your Thoughts

Colossians 1:16 (NIV): "For in him all things were created: things in heaven and on earth, visible and invisible, whether thrones or powers or rulers or authorities; all things have been created through him and for him."

Weekly Devotional

Everything in our lives was created by God. We take people and objects, sunsets and beaches, flowers and herbs for granted at times. The truth is that God took time to create all of these things. This week, take some time to just sit outside and bask in God's goodness and glory.

Journal Your Thoughts

Week 35

Proverbs 10:4 (NIV): "Lazy hands make for poverty, but diligent hands bring wealth."

Weekly Devotional

Laziness is a state of mind. God has created each of us to work. After Adam's encounter with God in the Garden of Eden, it has been man's responsibility to put his hand to the plow and work. As you continue this journey through the year, remember it's important to put your hand to the plow and work. This week, ask God to give you a strategy that is designed specifically for you and that will focus on accomplishing the will and purpose God has for your life.

Journal Your Thoughts

Matthew 7:7 (NKJV): "Ask, and it will be given to you; seek, and you will find; knock, and it will be opened to you."

Weekly Devotional

There may have been a time in your life when you were afraid to ask for something. One beautiful aspect of having a relationship with the Lord is that in any situation you can go to God and ask for anything you want. Now this does come with a warning. There are times when the answer will be "Yes," "No," or "Not yet." God takes time to groom us for what is needed for the kingdom here on earth. Begin to boldly ask God for what His will is and what your heart desires. Begin to boldly seek God and knock on His heavenly doors. Try these steps in the areas of your life that seem to be untouched or areas that you have not allowed God to intimately flow through.

Journal Your Thoughts

Proverbs 18:21 (NIV): "The tongue has the power of life and death, and those who love it will eat its fruit."

Weekly Devotional

The words you speak have an effect on current circumstances. Begin to speak life to every situation in your life right now. If you continue to speak negativity out of your mouth, negativity is exactly what you will get. Your tongue has more power than you think. Your tongue can change the status of any current situation you may encounter. I challenge you this week to only speak what is positive.

Journal Your Thoughts

Week 38

James 3:10 (NIV): "Out of the same mouth come praise and cursing. My brothers and sisters, this should not be."

Weekly Devotional

The tongue is such a powerful muscle and it's up to us to exercise it properly. As Christians, it is paramount that we speak life and God's light into a dark and dull world. It has been said, "What you nurture will grow." As God's people, we must continue to spread God's love to those around us. The temptation is there for us to demean and degrade others, but we must not yield to that temptation. Use your mouth to uplift and encourage others. As you go about this week, be cognizant of your speech and what comes out of your mouth.

Journal Your Thoughts

Week 39

Psalm 35:28 (NIV): "My tongue will proclaim your righteousness, your praises all day long."

Weekly Devotional

Our bodies were created to serve the Lord. As you begin to intentionally serve the Lord, take the time out throughout the day to proclaim God's goodness and greatness. Use your tongue to uplift and encourage those around you and proclaim God's good name to the world!

Journal Your Thoughts

Week 40

Jeremiah 30:2 (NLT): "This is what the Lord, the God of Israel, says: 'Write in a book all the words I have spoken to you.'"

Weekly Devotional

Every word the Lord speaks to us is so important that it must be written down. God speaks to us in many different ways. An inspiration might hit you as you're driving, or your child may say something wonderful that relates to their relationship with God and you've got to write it down immediately. This week be intentional about what you're writing down. Keep a journal handy so that when you're at home or out and about, you can write down information that God sends to you.

Journal Your Thoughts

Week 41

Job 19:23 (NKJV): "Oh, that my words were written! Oh, that they were inscribed in a book!"

Weekly Devotional

Weekly Devotional – In this scripture, Job speaks to the importance of having information written down. Job wanted to have the words after his death to live on and still have meaning. When buildings are built or reconstructed, typically a time capsule is left behind. Inside the time capsule are articles—items from the previous date and time period. When the time capsule is opened, decades or even centuries later, people can see what items were popular during that time. It is important to have your thoughts written on paper so that in the future, it can be referred to and uplift God's kingdom.

Journal Your Thoughts

Week 42

Deuteronomy 6:6-9 (NIV): "These commandments that I give you today are to be on your hearts. Impress them on your children. Talk about them when you sit at home and when you walk along the road, when you lie down and when you get up. Tie them as symbols on your hands and bind them on your foreheads. Write them on the doorframes of your houses and on your gates."

Weekly Devotional

One of the most notable passages in the Bible is the Ten Commandments. These scriptures were given to Moses after he went up on the mountain to speak face to face with God. God wants us to use these as commandments, not just as guides. These are of the utmost importance. The Ten Commandments are so important that they must be written down in prominent places in our homes, passed down to our children and memorized for our benefit. Anything of that magnitude must be ingrained in us.

Journal Your Thoughts

Psalm 102:18 (NKJV): "This will be written for the generation to come, That a people yet to be created may praise the Lord."

Weekly Devotional

This Psalm specifically indicates that what is written down will be available for the generations that are to follow. Written history is so important. When information is passed down from generation to generation as a part of history, it is better preserved when it is written down. As history progresses and life goes on, we should continue to write down our life events as they transpire so when we or our children look back on them, the generations that follow can praise the Lord. This week write down important personal events that will allow generations after you to see how far you've come and praise the Lord!

Journal Your Thoughts

Week 44

Psalm 100:4 (NKJV): "Enter into His gates with thanksgiving, And into His courts with praise. Be thankful to Him, and bless His name."

Weekly Devotional

Whenever we are in God's presence, we should enter and remain in praise. Oftentimes, we are downtrodden and sad because we are not thankful and walking in a spirit of praise. Change your attitude and you'll change your life! Make a commitment to change your thinking this week.

Journal Your Thoughts

Week 45

Thessalonians 5:18 (KJV): "In every thing give thanks: for this is the will of God in Christ Jesus concerning you."

Weekly Devotional

Thankfulness is a state of mind. It can be difficult to thank God in the middle of circumstances when they seem hard or overwhelming. As Christians, we are charged to give thanks to God in ALL things. Sure, difficult situations will occur, and those situations occur so that God can shape us and mold us into people who will assist with the building of God's kingdom here on earth.

Journal Your Thoughts

Week 46

Chronicles 16:34 (NKJV): "Oh, give thanks to the Lord, for He is good! For His mercy endures forever."

Weekly Devotional

"For His mercy endures forever." This is the great reason we should always give thanks to the Lord. When we analyze our current situations, no matter what they are, it is always time to give the Lord thanks. Whatever the situation is currently, it could have been so much worse. Think about the worst decision you have ever made. Do you realize had it not been for the Lord that situation could have been so much worse? Once we are able to sincerely thank God in the middle of a detrimental situation, our outcomes won't appear to be as catastrophic and God can show us exactly what we need. This week just say, "Thank you, Jesus."

Journal Your Thoughts

Week 47

Psalm 9:1 (NIV): "I will give thanks to you, LORD, with all my heart; I will tell of all your wonderful deeds."

Weekly Devotional

In our darkest hour, it is overwhelming how good God is to us. There have been times in my life when I've felt God was supposed to leave me, but instead God's presence was all over me. The time period between Thanksgiving and Christmas has traditionally been a challenging one. In this season, take some time to be alone with God. Take this time to bombard God's ear with your thankfulness. Tell the world of God's wonderful goodness.

Journal Your Thoughts

Week 48

Luke 2:7 (KJV): "And she brought forth her firstborn son, and wrapped him in swaddling clothes, and laid him in a manger; because there was no room for them in the inn."

Weekly Devotional

As you proceed through life, there will be times when you will feel as though there is no room for you. You will feel as though you're being pushed out of certain situations. Just ask Jesus: Where is that safe place that I can create for you and I? Our own safe time and location? That safe place will have everything you need and more than you could ever imagine.

Journal Your Thoughts

Luke 2:10 (NKJV): "Then the angel said to them, 'Do not be afraid, for behold, I bring you good tidings of great joy which will be to all people.'"

Weekly Devotional

Once the virgin Mary and her espoused husband, Joseph, were told by the angel that they were to be parents of the special baby Jesus and that He would be the Savior of the world, their outlook shifted. Whenever we are faced with a new challenge or an unusual circumstance, our first instinct is fear of the unknown or fear of what is coming next. As we move through this last month of the year and into the next year, let us move forward with a FEARLESS attitude. When we have Jesus with us and on our side, there is nothing we can't accomplish! This week lay aside any type of fear you are experiencing and remember to exercise your faith over your fear.

Journal Your Thoughts

Week 50

Isaiah 9:6 (KJV): "For unto us a child is born, unto us a son is given: and the government shall be upon his shoulder: and his name shall be called Wonderful, Counsellor, The mighty God, The everlasting Father, The Prince of Peace."

Weekly Devotional

Knowing that Jesus is the child that is born to US! This miracle child was born to save the world from sin and shame. This is the month we celebrate His birth. Take some time out to reflect on the birth of Jesus and what His birth means to you.

Journal Your Thoughts

Luke 2:11 (NKJV): "For there is born to you this day in the city of David a Savior, who is Christ the Lord."

Weekly Devotional

The promise of a Savior revealed in the Old Testament in the book of Isaiah had come true. Truly, unto us the Savior of the world was born. It is such a special blessing to know that Jesus was born. He was born and because He was born, He was able to die for our sins. We sometimes take the birth of Christ for granted and confuse it with gift giving. Jesus is the special gift that was given to the world. This week think about Jesus' life as a special gift that has been given to you.

Journal Your Thoughts

Week 52

Luke 2:14 (NKJV): "Glory to God in the highest, And on earth peace, goodwill toward men!"

Weekly Devotional

After Jesus' birth, this amazing declaration was made. This declaration acknowledged that the birth of our Savior had taken place and it was going to change the world.

Journal Your Thoughts

Made in the USA
Coppell, TX
17 November 2021

65937590R00036